Helen Huus
Professor of Education
University of Missouri-Kansas City

Robert J. Whitehead
Professor of Education
Sacramento State College

Program Director
Henry A. Bamman
Professor of Education
Sacramento State College

Addison-Wesley Publishing Company
Menlo Park, California   Reading, Massachusetts   London   Don Mills, Ontario

Roller Skates

Field Literature Program

ISBN 0–201–41207–1
 DEFGHIJ–DO

Acknowledgments

The order of acknowledgments follows the sequence of selections in the Table of Contents.
    Grateful acknowledgment is made to the following sources for permission to reprint copyrighted
material:

Wake Up, City! by Alvin Tresselt. Pictures by Roger Duvoisin. Reprinted by permission of Lothrop, Lee
& Shepard Co. © 1957 by Alvin Tresselt for text, by Roger Duvoisin for pictures.

"Timothy's Flower," from *Timothy's Flower* by Jean Van Leeuwen, Moneta Barnett, illustrator.
Copyright © 1967 by Jean Van Leeuwen. Reprinted by permission of Random House, Inc.

"The Park," from *I Live in a City* by James S. Tippett. Copyright 1927 by Harper & Brothers; renewed 1955
by James S. Tippett. Reprinted with permission of Harper & Row, Publishers, and Martha K. Tippett.

That's My Favorite by Dorothy Marino. Copyright © 1956 by Dorothy Marino. Reprinted in its
entirety by permission of J. B. Lippincott Company.

"The Ice-Cream Man," from *Taxis and Toadstools* by Rachel Field. Copyright 1926 by Doubleday &
Company, Inc. Reprinted by permission of the publisher.

Emilio's Summer Day by Miriam Anne Bourne. Selected illustrations by Ben Shecter. Copyright © 1966
by Miriam Anne Bourne. Copyright © 1966 by Ben Shecter. Reprinted with permission of Harper &
Row, Publishers.

"The Chimpanzee That Mopped the Floor," from *Zoo Babies* by William Bridges. Reprinted by
permission of William Morrow and Company, Inc., Publishers. Copyright © 1953 by William
Bridges.

"Bumble Bee," from *Nibble, Nibble* by Margaret Wise Brown. Copyright 1959 by William R. Scott, Inc.
Permission granted by the publisher, William R. Scott, Inc.

Hide and Seek Fog by Alvin Tresselt, illustrated by Roger Duvoisin. Reprinted by permission of Lothrop,
Lee & Shepard Co. Copyright © 1965 by Lothrop, Lee & Shepard Co., Inc.

"Where Go the Boats?" from *A Child's Garden of Verses* by Robert Louis Stevenson. Charles Scribner's
Sons (1905).

"Two Fawns," from *Dash and Dart* by Mary and Conrad Buff. Illustrations by Conrad Buff. Copyright
1942 by Mary Marsh Buff and Conrad Buff. Reprinted by permission of The Viking Press, Inc.

When I Go to the Moon by Claudia Lewis, illustrated by Leonard Weisgard. Reprinted with permission
of The Macmillan Company. © by Claudia Lewis 1961. © by Leonard Weisgard 1961.

"Wind Song" by Lilian Moore. Text copyright © 1967 by Lilian Moore. From *I Feel the Same Way*.
Used by permission of Atheneum Publishers.

"Pepito's Story," reprinted with the permission of Farrar, Straus & Giroux, Inc., from *Pepito's Story*
written and illustrated by Eugene Fern, copyright © 1960 by Eugene A. Fern.

"Afternoon with Grandmother" by Barbara A. Huff. Copyright © 1957 by Barbara A. Huff.

"Moy Moy's New Year," reprinted with the permission of Charles Scribner's Sons from *Moy Moy* by
Leo Politi. Illustrations by Leo Politi. Copyright © 1960 Leo Politi.

"Picnics," from the book *Around and About* by Marchette Chute. Copyright 1941 by Marchette Chute.
Copyright © 1957 by E. P. Dutton & Co., Inc. Used by permission of the publishers.

"In My Mother's House," from *In My Mother's House* by Ann Nolan Clark, illustrated by Velino
Herrera. Copyright 1941, copyright © renewed 1969 by Ann Nolan Clark. Reprinted by permission of
The Viking Press, Inc.

(Acknowledgments continued on page 224.)

Contents

Unit 1: City Streets

Unit 2: Worlds To Discover

Unit 3: Good Times Together

Unit 4: Witches and Fairies

Unit 5: Animals on Parade

Unit 6: Wonders Around You

Wake Up, City!
Alvin Tresselt

Under the stars the city sleeps. Only a
policeman is about, walking past the street
lamp. Only an alley cat, prowling a
backyard fence. Only a mother, singing her
baby back to sleep.

Then slowly the eastern sky begins to brighten. Here a light goes on . . . there a light goes on . . . The city sparrows begin to cheep. And the ducks on the pond in the park call to each other across the black water.

The city is waking in the dim gray dawn-light. The policeman sniffs the fresh morning air. "Ahh, a fine day it will be today," he says to himself.

The night train from far away pulls into the station, full of sleepy people. In the garage the buses are ready for their day's work. Their gas tanks are full and their windshields are clean. The bus drivers straighten their caps and hop into the buses.

In the harbor a great ocean liner comes in
on the morning tide. Busy tugboats pull it
up to the pier.

Down in the noisy markets men are
loading trucks with food. Crates of lettuce
and carrots. Boxes of oranges, bags of onions.
Fruits and vegetables from the farms. Fresh
food for the city to eat.

As the policeman walks back to his station
house he hears the *brrring* of alarm clocks.
A radio voice tells him today will be fair and
cooler. And he hears the babies crying for
their breakfast.

With a clank and a crunch and a rumble
the garbage trucks grind through the streets.
A sprinkler truck leaves a trail of shiny wet
pavement to catch the pink sky overhead.

The corner store is open, with stacks of
crisp newspapers piled up in front. Fair
and cooler, says the weather report, with
moderate winds. Barometer steady.

From open windows comes the smell of
perking coffee and sizzling bacon. The pop of
toasters, and the voices of mothers calling,
"Hurry up, you'll be late!"

Now the streets hum with the hustle and
bustle and jostle of the traffic. With a honk
and a toot and a start and a stop the trucks and
buses and taxis crowd through the busy streets.

Fathers are hurrying to their offices.
Mothers are making beds and washing dishes.
And the children have left for school.
Another day has begun.

GOOD MORNING!

14

Sharing Time

1. How do people travel in the city? How do trucks help the people in the city?

2. What do people in the story do to get ready for the new day?

3. How is early morning in this story like early morning where you live?

4. What do you do before you come to school?

5. How would you divide the story into four parts?

Timothy's Flower

Jean Van Leeuwen

Timothy lived in the city. In his block were Mrs. Olvera's candy store, Mr. Pepperoni's barber shop, Mr. Lane's laundry, and Mrs. Valdez. Mrs. Valdez always yelled at the boys. She warned them not to throw snowballs, not to roller-skate, and not to play ball against the apartment-house wall. The boys thought she was mean.

One summer day, Timothy's grandmother took him to a park. There he saw a yellow flower. The gardener at the park gave the flower to Timothy, who put it in an empty paper cup. When he got home, he set it out on the fire escape. He sat by his window and watched his flower, but it began to droop. Mr. Pepperoni gave him some plant food to put in the paper cup, but still the flower drooped. What could Timothy do to help his flower grow?

Timothy took his flower and went downstairs to sit in the sun.

The workmen had finished tearing down the building across the street. As Timothy watched, a truck full of bricks and boards rattled down the street and around the corner. Now the lot was empty.

Timothy watched the dust settling. The empty lot was big, so big that it would always have sun shining on it. He crossed the street and climbed over broken bricks to the middle of the lot.

With a stick he dug straight down. Sure enough, under the bricks there was dirt.

He dug a hole and carefully set his flower in it. Then he built a little wall of bricks around it.

Timothy sat and watched his flower until Rufus called him for supper.

"What were you doing?" asked Rufus,
as Timothy climbed over the bricks to
the street.

"Nothing," said Timothy, and he went
home to supper.

Every day Timothy watched his flower
grow taller and straighter. Its leaves stayed
very green. A bud began to open up into
a new yellow flower.

Then one morning a strange and very loud noise woke Timothy up. It was coming from the empty lot.

When he got downstairs, Timothy saw that the lot was not empty any more. In it were a huge yellow machine and some men wearing shiny helmets. The machine was making a grumbly, clanking noise and scooping up dirt with its sharp black teeth.

Timothy ran up to a big man in a red shirt and tugged on his sleeve.

"What's the matter, kid?" asked the man.

Timothy tugged on his sleeve until he had pulled him to the middle of the lot. He pointed to his flower.

The big man looked at Timothy's flower
and he looked at Timothy. Then he waved
his arms at the huge yellow machine. To
Timothy's surprise, the machine stopped
making its grumbly, clanking noise.

"Hey, Mike!" the big man shouted.
"Bring a shovel!"

Another man in a shiny helmet came
with a shovel.

Very carefully the big man dug up Timothy's flower. Very carefully he put it in Timothy's hands.

"It's a good thing you came along," he said. "We are digging up this whole lot for an apartment house."

He smiled. "You better beat it now," he said. "We have to keep digging."

Timothy climbed back to the street. The big man waved to the machine and it began to make its grumbly, clanking noise again.

Timothy crossed the street to the candy store.

"A raspberry ice so early in the morning?" asked Mrs. Olvera.

Timothy shook his head. "Could I please just have a cup?"

He put his flower in the cup. Then he carried it back to the steps and sat down.

Except for the huge yellow machine, everything was very quiet on Timothy's block.

It was too early for the boys to be playing ball. And it was too early for Mrs. Valdez to be yelling at them. She sat quietly in the window above Timothy, her fan going back and forth, back and forth.

Timothy sat and stared at his flower. He pressed it down in the cup and some dirt spilled out on the steps. He wished his grandmother would come today so he could take it back to the park.

A voice above him said, "What is that you are doing?"

Timothy looked up. It was Mrs. Valdez.

"Do you want to ruin the steps?" she scolded. "What have you got there?"

"It's a flower," said Timothy.

Mrs. Valdez stopped fanning herself and peered over the window sill. "I do not see so well," she said. "Would you hold it up?"

Timothy held his flower up high.

Mrs. Valdez nodded.

"It is most beautiful," she said. "When I was a girl in Puerto Rico, I had a whole garden of flowers. Now I just have this."

She pointed to something that Timothy had never noticed before. Outside Mrs. Valdez' window there was a window box. It was sagging a little and its green paint was peeling, but that did not matter. The window box was empty.

"Where did you find your beautiful flower?" asked Mrs. Valdez.

Timothy told her about the wonderful place that was the park. He told her about finding the flower and everything that had happened after that.

Then, for the first time Timothy could remember, Mrs. Valdez smiled.

"I have a wonderful idea," she said.

That afternoon Timothy and Mrs. Valdez took a walk. They walked to the Five-and-Ten on the next block. When they came back, Timothy was carrying a big brown bag, and so was Mrs. Valdez.

In Mrs. Valdez' apartment, Timothy opened the bags. He took out a can of bright-green paint, paint brushes, a plastic bag of fresh dirt, and two clay pots with flowers growing in them. Then he and Mrs. Valdez went to work.

Now on Timothy's block there is a window box freshly painted green. At one end are planted bright red geraniums. At the other end are bright pink petunias. And in the middle, growing tall and straight, is a yellow flower—Timothy's flower.

Every day Timothy and Mrs. Valdez watch it grow.

Sharing Time

1. Why did Timothy plant his flower in the empty lot?

2. How did all the people help Timothy with his flower?

3. Why do you think Timothy tried so hard to save his flower?

4. How did Timothy and Mrs. Valdez learn from each other?

5. Have you ever planted anything that grew? Tell about it.

The Park
James S. Tippett

I'm glad that I
  Live near a park

For in the winter
  After dark

The park lights shine
  As bright and still

As dandelions
  On a hill.

That's My Favorite

Dorothy Marino

One day a little girl named Suzy moved into a city apartment with her mother and father.

The next morning Suzy's mother and father were very busy getting settled in their new home. Suzy went downstairs to the sidewalk in front of the house to play hopscotch by herself. While she played Suzy was hoping some little city child might come along and want to play hopscotch with her.

And sure enough, it wasn't long before
she saw a little girl in a red hat and blue coat
coming from way down the street. She
stopped beside Suzy to watch her and in a
few minutes both were playing hopscotch.

The little girl said, "I like to play hopscotch.
That's my favorite."

When Suzy's mother called her for lunch
she went upstairs, happy that she had found
a playmate.

In the afternoon Suzy took some chalk
and drew the hopscotch again on the
sidewalk. She hoped her playmate would
come. Sure enough, it wasn't long before she
saw a little girl in red hat and blue coat coming
from way down the street, skipping rope
as she came.

She stopped beside Suzy and Suzy asked,
"Would you like to play hopscotch?"

"I don't especially like to play hopscotch,"
said the little girl. "Would you like to jump
rope with me?"

Suzy looked surprised but said, "All right."

They took turns jumping. "I like to jump
rope," said Suzy's playmate. "That's
my favorite."

When her mother called, Suzy went
upstairs, happy to have a playmate. "But
I would like to know which is really her
favorite," she thought to herself.

That night Suzy's daddy went down to
the corner store and bought a jumping rope.

Early the next morning Suzy was down in
front of the house jumping rope. She hoped
her playmate would come again.

Sure enough it wasn't long before she
saw a little girl in red hat and blue coat
coming from way down the street, roller
skating as she came.

She stopped beside Suzy and Suzy asked,
"Would you like to jump rope?"

"I don't especially like to jump rope,"
said the little girl. "Would you like to
roller skate with me?"

Suzy looked surprised but said, "All right."

Suzy went upstairs to get her skates and
they skated up and down the sidewalk
all morning.

"I like to skate," said Suzy's playmate.
"That's my favorite."

When Suzy's mother called her for lunch she went upstairs. She was still happy that she had found a playmate, but more puzzled than ever to know what was really the girl's favorite.

In the afternoon Suzy took her skates down again and skated back and forth. She hoped her playmate would come along soon.

Sure enough it wasn't long before she saw a little girl in red hat and blue coat coming from way down the street. She was pushing a doll carriage.

The little girl stopped beside Suzy. Suzy said, "Would you like to roller skate with me?"

"I don't especially like to roller skate," said the little girl. "Would you like to play dolls with me?"

Suzy looked surprised but said, "All right."

Suzy brought out her doll carriage and the girls played with dolls all afternoon.

"I like to play with dolls," said Suzy's playmate. "That's my favorite."

When it was time to go up, Suzy's mother came down to help her with the doll carriage.

The next morning Suzy wondered what toy to take down with her. Whatever she chose, her playmate would surely say she didn't like it.

At last she decided to watch from the window to see if her playmate would come along. Sure enough it wasn't long before she saw a little girl in red hat and blue coat coming from way down the street.

As Suzy watched, the little girl stopped, pulled some chalk from her pocket and began to draw the hopscotch on the sidewalk.

"She's playing hopscotch," Suzy called
to her mother as she grabbed her coat and
ran out the apartment door.

In the hall she paused to look down again.
She was very pleased and surprised. Beside the
little girl in red hat and blue coat playing
hopscotch was a little girl in red hat and blue
coat jumping rope and they looked just alike.

Suzy hurried down to the next floor and
stopped again to look out the window. She
was even more pleased and surprised. Down on
the sidewalk were three little girls. One was
playing hopscotch. One was jumping rope.
One was roller skating. And they all looked
just alike.

Suzy hurried down the last flight of stairs, ran through the hall and out the door. There on the sidewalk were four little girls. One who played hopscotch, one who jumped rope, one who roller skated and one who played with dolls, and they all looked just alike.

Suzy's new friends were quadruplets!

Sharing Time

1. What was the surprise in the story?

2. How were the four girls alike and how were they different?

3. If the children had been boys, what would be different in the story?

4. What do you do to be a good playmate for your friends?

The Ice-Cream Man
Rachel Field

When summer's in the city,
    And brick's a blaze of heat,
The Ice-Cream Man with his little cart
    Goes trundling down the street.

Beneath his round umbrella,
    Oh, what a joyful sight,
To see him fill the cones with mounds
    Of cooling brown and white:

Vanilla, chocolate, strawberry,
    Or chilly things to drink
From bottles full of frosty-fizz,
    Green, orange, white, or pink.

His cart might be a flower bed
    Of roses and sweet peas,
The way the children cluster round
    As thick as honeybees.

Emilio's Summer Day
Miriam Anne Bourne

Emilio sat on the front stoop under the summer sun. It was a hot morning. If I spit on the sidewalk, it will sizzle, Emilio thought. He tried it. Along the street came Mr. Martinez. He stopped in front of his car. "Going to polish her?" Emilio asked Mr. Martinez.

Mr. Martinez wiped his forehead on a sleeve.

"No, boy," he said. "Too hot today."

Emilio walked around the corner to the playground. Willie's big brother was there playing catch with his friend. "You seen Willie?" Emilio asked.

"No," said Willie's brother.

The slide was too hot to slide down. Emilio sat on a swing, closed his eyes, and let go, feeling the rush of air against his face. The chains burned his hands. Emilio jumped off and walked home.

For lunch there was soup. "On a day like this—" he asked, "soup?"

"Soup," said his mother, "is what we've got."

After lunch Emilio's mother gave him some money. "Buy a loaf of bread," she said.

"And a candy bar?" he asked.

"Okay."

He walked slowly along the sidewalk to the store, past Neighborhood House where his brother went to dances and his sister went to Brownies.

Some girls in Emilio's class were sitting on the steps. "Emilio, 'milio, 'milio," they teased. He walked by quickly.

At the corner Emilio stopped to watch a fire engine clang by. Afterward it was quiet except for the far-off sound of the cars on the bridge.

Emilio crossed the street to the next block, where the store was. It was dark and cool inside. Emilio bought the bread. Then he looked at the candy bars. It was hard to choose. They all looked good.

Emilio took a chocolate bar quickly, before he could change his mind, and paid the storekeeper.

"Some hot day," said the storekeeper.

"Uh-*HUH*," agreed Emilio.

Going home, he walked on the other side of the street. The candy bar was soft from the heat. The melted chocolate stuck to his fingers, and Emilio licked them clean.

No one was in the vacant lot. He looked in his secret hole. Inside was a ball of string, three nails, and a pack of baseball cards. Still safe, Emilio thought. He covered them up and walked home.

Emilio gave his mother the loaf of bread. He watched his grandmother open the birdcage to feed the parakeets. "Poor things," she sighed. "It's so hot they can hardly breathe."

"Here," said Emilio. "Let me do it."

The birds pecked listlessly at the seeds. Emilio stroked their blue and yellow feathers before closing the cage door.

Emilio went upstairs, disgusted. He
kicked open the door to the roof. High
overhead he saw his mother's wash. It hung
limp in the still air. Emilio squinted into the
sun and saw his red shirt and his sister's
white church dress.

The smell of coffee cooking drifted from
one of the windows. What I'd like, thought
Emilio, is a cup of orange ice. He licked his
lips, remembering the taste.

Emilio ran down three flights of stairs to
the street. When he went outside, the sun
almost knocked him down, it was so hot.

Emilio leaned against the door frame,
looking for something to watch. He looked
at the windows across the street. There was
someone leaning out of every window. On
every stoop there were people hardly talking,
scarcely moving except to fan themselves
or wipe their faces.

If I had an egg, Emilio thought, I'd drop
it on the stoop and watch it fry. But he had no
egg. And he knew what his mother would
say if he asked her for one.

The sun was lower in the sky. It beat down
hotter and hotter—on the house, on the
sidewalk, on the stoop, where Emilio waited
for something to happen.

He felt his damp shirt sticking to his damp back. He smelled orange peel in an open garbage can. Around the corner he heard a car start. Music floated out of the windows across the street. A baby cried. But nothing moved.

Then, faintly at first, far down the street came a new sound.

Emilio listened hard as the sound came nearer and nearer.

It was a motor sound like that of a big truck, and a swishing sound, and the noise of shrieking, laughing children. Emilio ran onto the sidewalk to see what was coming.

"STREET WASHER!" he yelled at the top of his lungs.

Soon the street was filled with the children
from his block. Out of the doors they poured,
down the steps, from up the street and
behind buildings.

They shouted and screamed as the street
washer came to a halt and sprayed them
with icy water.

On the back of his neck Emilio felt the
shock of chilly water. He whirled around and
saw Willie grinning at him. Emilio bent down
to splash back, cutting the stream of water
toward Willie. "Take that!" he shouted.

After the truck left, the children waded
in the puddles that had settled in the street.

Later, as Emilio watched from a window,
the puddles caught the last of the summer
light. And over his head, behind his house,
the sun slipped away for the night.

Sharing Time

1. What made the children
   happy at the end of the
   story?

2. Who lived on Emilio's street?

3. What made you think it was
   a hot day?

4. How do you cool off on a
   hot day?

The Chimpanzee That Mopped the Floor

William Bridges

One day a man was walking through the jungle in Africa and he saw a little black animal running along the path ahead of him. "Why, that looks like a baby chimpanzee!" he said to himself.

He ran to catch up with it and, sure enough, it *was* a baby chimpanzee, all fuzzy-haired and only a few weeks old.

The baby was hungry and frightened, for it was lost and didn't know where to find its father or mother. And since the jungle is very, very big, the man didn't know where to find them either, so he put the baby on his shoulders and started home. All the way the baby chimpanzee rode on the man's shoulder with one arm around his neck and one hand holding on to his hair.

52

When the man's wife saw the baby, she
said, "I am going to name her Josephine,
and she can live in our house. She can sleep
in the rocking chair on the front porch and
play in the yard all day."

So they gave Josephine a bottle of warm
milk and put her to bed in the rocking chair.
Every day she played in the yard in the hot
African sunshine, and she grew bigger and
stronger. Sometimes she would go into the

house and watch the people as they were
sweeping or mopping the floor or making
beds or cooking. When she would try to catch
the broom, or slide on the wet floor, or climb
onto the bed, or taste something that was
cooking, the people would say, "No, no,
Josephine! Bad girl! You go out and play
in the yard."

Finally the people decided to move to
another house where there was no room for
Josephine, and they wanted to find her a good
home. So they sent her to the Bronx Zoo.

It was very different in the zoo from living in a house, and playing in the sunshine all day long, and sleeping in a rocking chair. At first, because there was no room for her anywhere else, she lived in the zoo's Animal Hospital.

Josephine wasn't sick, so she didn't have to stay in a cage and take medicine. Every morning her cage was opened, and she was allowed to play in the hall while the keeper mopped the floor. First he would draw a bucket of warm water, and Josephine would climb up on a stool to watch him when he turned the faucet on. She always jumped when the water went splashing into the bucket. Then she followed him down the hall to the closet to get the mop.

At first she was afraid of the mop, because she had never been allowed to touch one in her home in Africa. After a while she learned that the keeper was not going to send her away or scold her, so she began to try to catch the mop as it went *swish-swish-swish* across the floor. Sometimes she really would catch it, and then she pushed the heavy mop forward and backward, just as if she were trying to help.

"Why don't you give Josephine a mop of her own and let her mop the floor for you while you do something else?" the doctor asked the keeper one morning. He was only joking, but the keeper thought it would be fun to see what would happen. So he found a short piece of broom handle and tied a rag on the end of it. Then he filled a pan with warm water and put a sponge in it.

"You're my helper, Josephine," he said.
"You mop the floors and I'll wash the
windows."

That was the first time in her whole life
that Josephine ever had a mop and a pan of
water and a sponge to do anything she liked
with. First she bent over and tasted the water.
Then she tasted the mop. Then she put
the mop in the water and got it all wet. Next
she squeezed the sponge, the way the keeper
always did. And finally, to everybody's
surprise, she stood up and swished her own
little mop back and forth on the floor!

But I am sorry to say that Josephine didn't do a very good job of mopping the whole floor. She mopped just one tiny spot, and then she wet the mop and scrubbed the same spot all over again. At last she got tired of doing that, so she emptied the water on the floor and put the pan on her head like a hat.

After that, the keeper didn't tell her she could be his helper any more. He always mopped the floor himself. And when people asked him why he didn't let Josephine help him, he always said to them, "Josephine is the cleanest little chimpanzee I ever saw. When she mops the floor, she uses a whole pan of water for one tiny little spot. I don't let her help me any more because I would have to spend all morning carrying pans of water to her!"

Sharing Time

1. How did the man and his wife care for Josephine?

2. How was Josephine's life in the zoo different from her life with the man and his wife?

3. What did Josephine do when she was given a mop of her own?

4. How was Josephine like a small child?

5. What useful things can pets do?

Bumble Bee

Margaret Wise Brown

Black and yellow
Little fur bee
Buzzing away
In the timothy
Drowsy
Browsy
Lump of a bee
Rumbly
Tumbly
Bumbly bee.
Where are you taking
Your golden plunder
Humming along
Like baby thunder?
Over the clover
And over the hay
Then over the apple trees
Zoom away.

Hide and Seek Fog

Alvin Tresselt

The lobsterman first saw the fog as it
rolled in from the sea. He watched it turn off
the sun-sparkle on the waves, and he saw
the water turn gray. Carefully he set his last
lobster pot, and headed his boat back to
shore.

The dampness touched the crisp white
sails of the racing sailboats, and suddenly
the wind left them in the middle of the race.

The sailboats had to creep home around the
islands and across the bay, ahead of the
rolling fog.

In long straight lines the seagulls and terns
flew back to their roosts on the craggy rocks.
They knew the fog was coming, too.

Now the water of the bay was gray like
the sky, and the end of the beach was gone.
Now the afternoon sun turned to a pale
daytime moon, then vanished into the bank
of fog.

On the beach, the sand was suddenly cold
and sticky. The mothers and fathers gathered
up blankets and picnic baskets. They called—
"Cathy! John! Come out of the water!
We're going now!"

The children ran in and out one more time, blue-lipped and shivering. They scurried about looking for lost pails and shovels. They scooped up one more pretty shell and a gray seagull feather. Then everyone trudged across the chilly sand and cold rocks, back to cars and cottages.

The lobsterman delivered his lobsters to the fishing wharf. He hurried home through winding streets, just as the fog began to hide the town.

The sailboats bobbled like corks on the dull gray water of the cove. Their sails were wrapped for the night, and the sailors rowed through the misty fog back to land.

But indoors in the seaside cottages the

children toasted marshmallows over a driftwood fire, while the fog tip-toed past the windows and across the porch.

And the fog stayed three days.

On the first day the lobsterman spent his time painting buoys and mending lobster pots. He could hear the mournful lost voices of the foghorns calling across the empty grayness of the bay.

The fathers read books and took naps. Then they got out their cars and drove the mothers into town so they could do their marketing . . . creeping, creeping . . . along the strange and hidden roads. The streets of the town were so full of fog that the people bumped into one another with their arms full of bundles.

Only the children liked the fog. They
played hide-and-seek in and out among the
gray-wrapped rocks. They spoddled in the
lazy lapping waves on the beach, and they
got lost—right in front of their own cottages!

On the second day the lobsterman talked
about the weather down on the fishing wharf.
"The worst fog in twenty years," the
lobsterman said. And no one could go out
after fish.

The fathers scowled and complained about spending their vacations in the middle of a cloud. The mothers tried to cheer everyone up. They put on gay bright clothes, and they helped the children make scrapbooks by the driftwood fire.

But out of doors the fog twisted about the cottages like slow-motion smoke. It dulled the rusty scraping of the beach grass. It muffled the chattery talk of the low tide waves. And it hung, wet and dripping, from the bathing suits and towels on the clothesline.

Then on the third afternoon there was suddenly a warm glow in the foggy air. And before everyone's eyes the damp cotton-wool thinned out. The western sun slanted through, under the fog, changing the islands

in the bay to gold. A breeze sprang up out
of no place and gently, gently, rolled back
the fog, back to the wide and empty ocean.
Once more the water sparkled, beyond the
islands, across the wide bay to the edge of
the world.

The lobsterman went down to check his
boat and make sure that everything was all
ready for the morning. The sailors made plans
for a sailboat race next day, in and out among
the islands.

Then at last the mothers and fathers and
all the children came out of the shut-in
cottages into the fresh, clean air. And the
families gathered for a clambake on the beach.

Sharing Time

1. What did the people do when they saw the fog coming?

2. What did the people do while the fog lasted?

3. How did the fog make people feel?

4. What parts of the story help you picture what the fog was like?

5. What would *you* do if the fog came and stayed for three days?

Where Go the Boats?

Robert Louis Stevenson

Dark brown is the river,
    Golden is the sand.
It flows along forever,
    With trees on either hand.

Green leaves a-floating,
    Castles of the foam,
Boats of mine a-boating—
    Where will all come home?

On goes the river
    And out past the mill,
Away down the valley,
    Away down the hill.

Away down the river,
    A hundred miles or more,
Other little children
    Shall bring my boats ashore.

Two Fawns
Mary and Conrad Buff

The forest is great.
It is big.
It is dark.
Tall trees sway overhead.
They bend their branches down
As if they want to look at something,
Something in the fern bed,
Something lying in the green ferns.

The something in the fern bed
Is a baby,
A baby deer,
The color of a rusty nail
Spotted with white,
A little rusty-colored fawn
Lying in the green ferns.

The little fawn is very new.
He has just come.
He has just been born
This early morning.
The little fawn looks up,
Looks up into the tree tops overhead.
He is alone
In the fern bed
In the forest.
The little rusty-colored fawn
Sees the fern leaves
Playing with the wind.

He sees a little squirrel
With a bushy tail
And two black-bead eyes
Looking back at him.
He sees a butterfly
Resting on a fern leaf,
White wings opening,
White wings shutting.

Dash, the fawn, looks and wonders.
He looks and wonders
At all the things he sees.

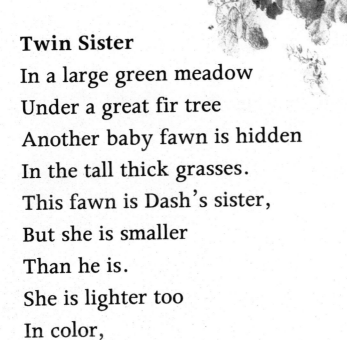

Twin Sister
In a large green meadow
Under a great fir tree
Another baby fawn is hidden
In the tall thick grasses.
This fawn is Dash's sister,
But she is smaller
Than he is.
She is lighter too
In color,
And covered with white spots
Like her brother.

Mother Doe

Dash hears a soft call.
It is his mother Doe
Calling to him
As she comes bounding between
The great trees of the forest.
She comes to feed her baby.
She comes to feed little Dash.
She lies beside him.
She licks his soft brown fur.
Now he is safe,
Safe with his mother,
His wise, strong mother.

Dash is hungry.
He pushes against his mother
To tell her he is hungry.
When milk comes
Dribbling slowly down his throat,
It is warm,
It is good.
But soon there is no more.

Dash butts his mother
With his wet black nose.
He butts her hard
Again and again.
He wants more milk,
But there is no more.

Dash Stands Up

Dash tries to stand.
Up he goes
On his thin wobbly legs.
He trembles and shakes
And falls down among the fern leaves.
He tries again.
Up he goes.
He falls down again.

It is hard to stand up
When one is so young.
Dash tries and tries
Until he is too tired to try any more.

Then he snuggles close
To comforting Mother Doe.
He closes his eyes,
His big brown eyes,
And goes to sleep,
Sound asleep,
Hard asleep.

Mother Doe does not sleep.
She stays awake.
She looks and listens.
She smells the air
With her black nose.
She is guarding her fawn baby.
She watches as he sleeps.
She guards him from danger.

Learning Things

Each day Dash learns something new.
He learns to stand
On his thin wobbly legs
And not fall down.

He learns to walk.
He learns to run.
He learns to jump.
When he is two weeks old
He can hop over little bushes.

He follows his mother
Here and there and about,
Watching her.
Dart watches her too,
Doing the things she does,
Running from the things she does,
Both fawns learning from her.

Sounds

Mother Doe is teaching her babies.
They learn about sounds.
In the great forest
There are many kinds.
There are near-by sounds.
There are far-off sounds.
There are new dangerous sounds.
There are old safe ones.

The fawns listen.
Sometimes they run away
And sometimes they hide just where they are.
The white spots on their rusty backs
Look like spots of sunshine
Falling on the brown earth.
The bears and the mountain lions,
The gray wolves and the coyotes
Cannot see them
Unless they move.
As long as the fawns stay quiet
No animal can see them.
They are safe.
They have no smell
When they are little.
Only their mother can smell them,
Only their mother can trail them
With her wet black nose
As they lie deep among the fern leaves.

Sharing Time

1. What did Dash and Dart learn from their mother?

2. How did Mother Doe take care of the fawns?

3. Why were the fawns safe if they stayed quiet?

4. How are Dash and Dart like other baby animals you know?

When I Go to the Moon

Claudia Lewis

When I go to the moon
I'll let the scientists explore the craters.
What I want to see is the earth.
I want to look back—
No, not back, but up—
At that great lighted ball,
This world,
That will float there among the old stars
Like a newly created moon.

Imagine the size of it!

Four times larger than the moon we know
And eighty times more bright,
Lighting the moonscape
With white earthlight,
A giant globe up in the sky,
Slowly turning as a globe turns,
With North and South America
And Africa
There before my eye.
Why, the whole thing will seem
    like a mistake!

    Imagine the colors!
I'll see them if I look through telescopes
    and filters—
Deserts dusty red,
Green fields
And dark green patches that are forest trees,
The North Pole white with ice
And flash! the sunlight
Striking on the seas.
The earth will look like a giant unimaginable
Christmas tree ornament!

Actually,
There's only one sea
Up on that globe—
All the oceans are one,
None bounded
By any dyke or wall,
All, the homes of fish leaping and splashing,
Fish that could easily swim from one
    to the other.
"Earth" they call it—
Why not "Ocean"?
It's clear to me
There's not as much land up there
As sea.

I'll sit on a moon mountain
And look at the shores of Maine
    and the Oregon shores.
I'll know that children are there, wading
And playing on the long sandy beaches,
Each child thinking he has come to the edge
    of the earth.

I'll wonder how it can be that there are
    people in Maine
Who have never seen the people of Oregon—
Only inches to travel!
And can it be that some Australians
Stay on their little island all of their lives?

    I'll watch the world turning,
Watch the night fall,
Part of the earth still burning bright
While my continent up there
Moves slowly around
To the dark side
Away from the sun's light.

    I'll know that a million eyes are
    turned to look, then, at the moon where
    I am,
Old moon in the earth's skies,
    queen of the heavens—

I'll know the eyes are watching—
Back and forth we'll stare across
    the cosmic miles,
The electric seas of space
Where rockets are in flight—
Oh you up there, I'll say, I see you,
I know you're there,
I know how you are walking
    out under the street lights,
I know the children are lying in their beds
    watching the moon through the windows—
Do you know I am thinking of you?

Goodnight, Earth, I'll say,
Then I'll lie down in my spaceman's bed.
The night will be
As still as stone.

But I'll know that while I sleep
The moon is circling round
And gently pulling at earth's seas.
The tides are moving
On the shores at home.

The earth is near.
Goodnight, I'll say,
All's well here,
Is all well there?

Sharing Time

1. What does the earth look like from the moon?

2. What happens at night on the earth?

3. Who do you think is telling this story?

4. How is this story like the line "I see the moon, and the moon sees me"?

5. Would you like to go to the moon? Tell why or why not.

Wind Song
Lilian Moore

When the wind blows
The quiet things speak.
Some whisper, some clang,
Some creak.

Grasses swish.
Treetops sigh.
Flags slap
and snap at the sky.
Wires on poles
whistle and hum.
Ashcans roll.
Windows drum.

When the wind goes—
suddenly
then,
the quiet things
are quiet again.

Good Times Together

Pepito's Story

Eugene Fern

Padingo was a little town by the sea.
The children who lived there spent their
time fishing, swimming, and playing
games. All except Pepito, who loved to
dance. When he danced, he could be a
clown, a seagull, the wind itself, or
anything he wanted to be. But he was
unhappy, for no one would dance with
him. His grandmother was the only one
who understood him. When he was
unhappy, she could make him feel
better by saying a little rhyme.

On a hill in Padingo lived Don
Esquadrille and his only daughter
Estrellita. He was rich and proud and
had just been made the Lord Mayor of
Padingo. He thought Estrellita was much
too grand to play with the other
children. So she had no one to play
with at all.

Poor little Estrellita! She had all the dolls
and toys a girl could desire, and not a soul
to share them with. Sometimes she would
stand and look out her window at the sea,
remembering the good times she had had
playing with the other children, before her
father had become Lord Mayor of Padingo.

Day after day went by, until she became
quite ill, and had to be put to bed. Don
Esquadrille called in all sorts of doctors, but
none of them could tell what the matter was,
so all their remedies failed. The poor child

grew thinner and weaker by the day. At last
her father asked if there was anything at all he
could do to make her feel better. Estrellita
replied, "Yes, Father. I would like to see my
friends—the children who live by the sea."

Without further ado, Don Esquadrille set
off for the town square. He gathered all the
children together and told them of Estrellita's
wish. He asked them to come to his house,
and urged each child to bring some gift to
cheer her up. "Perhaps if she had a real
friend," he said to himself, "she would try to
get well."

The children scurried off in all directions in search of presents. They loved Estrellita, and each child hoped that his gift would be the one to make her raise her head and smile. Only Pepito stood there uncertainly, wondering what to do.

Pepito and his grandmother were very poor, and the boy could think of nothing he could give Estrellita. As he trudged sadly home, Pepito remembered that he had a special reason for loving Estrellita. Of all the children in Padingo, she alone had never made fun of his dancing.

If only he could think of some way to help her! He thought and thought, and when he could think no more, he started to cry.

When his grandmother heard what was the matter, she said, "No doll or toy will make Estrellita well. What she needs is something very special—something you alone can give." And taking him in her arms, she repeated the little rhyme:

If every child were like every other,
You wouldn't know who was your sister
   or brother;
And if every flower looked just the same,
"Flower" would have to be each flower's
   name.

This time Pepito nodded, for all at once he
had an idea.

Drying his eyes and standing up tall,
Pepito marched up the hill that led to the
home of Don Esquadrille. He knocked firmly
at the big front door, and soon he was
standing in a hall filled with children, all
holding in their arms the gifts they had
brought for Estrellita.

One by one the children tiptoed into
Estrellita's bedroom and presented their gifts.
Estrellita thanked them all very nicely, and

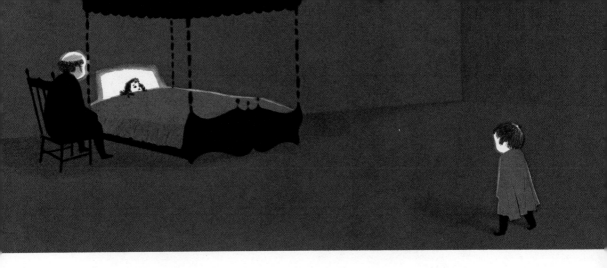

they tiptoed quietly out. Don Esquadrille
watched her face hopefully . . . but it was as
sad and pale as ever.

Just then, in walked Pepito, alone as
usual. His hands were empty, but he was
smiling. He looked at Estrellita, quite lost in
the big bed, her little face almost the color of
the pillow. His dark eyes glowed with feeling,
but he said nothing. Instead, he started
to dance.

Pepito danced as he had never danced
before! Into his dancing he poured everything
in his heart: the loneliness of the little girl
living on the hill, his own loneliness among
the other children, his sorrow that she was
sick, and his hope that she would soon be
well and able to play with her friends again.

As he danced, a strange thing happened.
Estrellita began to smile, at first only with her
eyes, but soon it was with her whole face.
All of a sudden she laughed, clapped her
hands, and sat up in bed.

A moment later she had thrown back the
cover and jumped to the floor. No sooner was
she on her feet than she began to dance with
Pepito! Don Esquadrille rubbed his eyes, but
when he saw that it was really true, that his
beloved daughter was well again, he was so
overjoyed that he joined hands with the two
children and began to dance himself!

Never had the house on the hill been filled
with such joy! The Lord Mayor was happy
once more because Estrellita was well, and

because he had learned something: that no
amount of presents can take the place of real
friendship.

From that night on, Estrellita could play
with anyone she liked, and she was never
lonely or sick again. She spent long days
by the sea with her many friends—but most
of all with her special friend, Pepito.

As for Pepito, well . . . he was happiest of
all, for he had learned that his dancing could
bring people joy. He knew that each one of

us had something all his own to give to the world, and at last he understood what his grandmother's little rhyme meant:

If every child were like every other,
You wouldn't know who was your sister
    or brother;
And if every flower looked just the same,
"Flower" would have to be each flower's
    name.

And he thought to himself, "How dull that would be! I'm glad I'm a dancer! I'm glad to be me!"

Sharing Time

1. How did Estrellita's father try to help her get well?

2. Tell about Pepito's gift to Estrellita.

3. What lesson did Don Esquadrille learn? What lesson did Pepito learn?

4. What would you have given Estrellita?

5. How can you show other children that you are friendly?

Afternoon with Grandmother
Barbara A. Huff

I always shout when Grandma comes,
But Mother says, "Now please be still
And good and do what *Grandma* wants."
And I say, "Yes, I will."

So off we go in Grandma's car.
"There's a brand new movie quite near by,"
She says, "that I'd rather like to see."
And I say, "So would I."

The show has horses and chases and battles;
We gasp and hold hands the whole way
    through.
She smiles and says, "I liked that lots."
And I say, "I did, too."

"It's made me hungry, though," she says,
"I'd like a malt and tarts with jam.
By any chance are you hungry, too?"
And I say, "Yes, I am."

Later at home my Mother says,
"I hope you were careful to do as bid.
Did you and Grandma have a good time?"
And I say, "YES, WE DID!!!"

Moy Moy's New Year
Leo Politi

Moy Moy is a little Chinese girl. She
lives in Los Angeles with her father and
mother and three brothers—Peter,
Johnny, and Tommy. They live over their
father's shop on Chanking Street.

The Chinese New Year is coming, and
so Chanking Street is decorated. People
hang *lay-shee*, or good-luck money, over
their doorways. Moy Moy's brothers
make a New Year's card for her as a
surprise. Charlie, a kind and friendly
man, is in charge of the children's parade.
He shows the children how to do the lion
dance. Peter dances the lion's head, and
Johnny dances the tail. At first Moy Moy
is afraid of the lion. But then she looks
underneath it and sees how Peter holds
up the lion's head. Moy Moy can hardly
wait for the day of the parade.

At last New Year's Day comes. All the people greet each other.

"Gung Ho Sun Nin!"

"Happy New Year!"

The boys give Moy Moy the card they have made for her.

恭 賀 新 年　　妹 妹
Happy　New　Year　Moy Moy

Soon the children come together for the parade. The girls wear lovely silk costumes. The boys wear bright costumes with colored bands around their legs. Charlie wears his mandarin suit and is busy getting the parade started. Even the lion is dressed up. He is decorated with trimmings and tassels.

The parade begins. The children with flags walk first. Then comes Moy Moy's brother Tommy, wearing a mask. He teases

and leads the mighty lion along the way. The
lion is followed by the band, and by girls
carrying banners and lanterns.

Moy Moy is at the very end of the parade.
She carries a big peacock lantern. She is the
smallest child in the parade.

Rat-a-tat, rat-a-tat! Firecrackers are set off
from all sides. The noise grows louder and
louder, as the lion dances through the streets.

Suddenly the lion pretends he is tired and
lies down on the pavement. The children
laugh as they watch the expressions on his

face. At last he closes his droopy eyes and falls asleep.

But when the music begins to play the lion awakes and is on his feet and on his way again.

The lion stops to dance in front of each shop. After a short dance he looks up at the lay-shee money hanging in the doorway. Then he opens his huge mouth and swallows it.

All the money the lion collects is used for children's parties, and to buy them toys. This is a New Year's gift from the shopkeepers, because they love the children and want to make them happy.

As the lion comes near Moy Moy's shop she runs upstairs. Mother lets Moy Moy hold out the lay-shee money from the balcony. To tease the lion Moy Moy holds the money up so he cannot reach it. This makes him furious and everyone laughs. The lion pretends to try to climb up the wall. After that he reaches high and swallows the money.

When the parade is over the children
have a big party. There are delicious Chinese
cookies and candies, and toys for everyone.

Charlie knows which toys the children
like and have been wishing for. He gives
something to each one.

A story book for Dorothy and a fan for Mary.

A drum for Ronny. A trumpet for Gary.
A toy horse for Willy.

Nancy, who likes to play tricks on people,
gets a toy snake that springs at you from a
box. And Jim has fun with his tiger puppet.

Moy Moy's brothers get kites, for kite
flying begins with the New Year. Peter and
Johnny have a green dragon kite. It is so big
that it will take both of them to fly it.

Now it is Moy Moy's turn. She holds out
her little hands and Charlie puts into
them—a Chinese doll. It is the doll that she
has seen so often in Mr. Fong's toy shop.
Moy Moy hugs the doll close. Now it is her
very own!

That night the street is crowded. People come from everywhere to see the dragon parade. The street is bright with many lights and with lanterns.

Moy Moy and her brothers watch the parade from the balcony of a friend's house. Her father is in the dragon parade.

The music begins to play and along the street comes a huge dragon. The dragon is so long that the children cannot see where the tail ends. And it is so tall that as it passes the balcony they can reach out and almost touch it.

No wonder it is so tall, it is held up with poles by hundreds of men. Its body moves like waves in a stormy sea.

If Moy Moy had not known it was a make-believe dragon she might have thought it was some strange creature from another world.

Mother tells the children that when she was a little girl in China she saw a dragon parade. The dragon's head was as high as the roof tops. It was held up by three acrobats standing on each other's shoulders.

The children watch with wonder as thousands of firecrackers are set off in the public square. They make bright patterns against the darkness of the night. It is the greatest burst of light and noise Moy Moy has ever heard, and she puts her hands over her ears.

When the festival is over, Moy Moy and
her mother and brothers go home. Moy
Moy's brothers take turns and carry her
piggy-back all the way.

People leaving the street give New Year's
greetings to each other.

Everyone says to Moy Moy,
"Gung Ho Sun Nin, Moy Moy!"
"Happy New Year, Moy Moy!"

Sharing Time

1. What did Tommy and Moy Moy do in the parade?

2. How did the lion help the children get to have parties and toys?

3. Why was Moy Moy happy after the parade?

4. What would you have done if you had seen the dragon parade?

5. What holiday festivals do you have?

Picnics

Marchette Chute

Sunshine and wieners and pickles and ham,
    Not enough salt for the eggs,
Marshmallows cooked on the end of a stick,
    Ants crawling over our legs.

Candy and cookies and peanuts and cake,
    Finding the frosting has run,
All of us knowing we've eaten too much—
    Picnics are certainly fun!

In My Mother's House
Ann Nolan Clark

Home

This is my Mother's house;
My Father made it.
He made it with adobe bricks;
He made it strong;
He made it big;
He made it high;
My Mother's house,
I live in it.

This is my Mother's house;
My Mother plastered it
With brown clay;
On the outside
My Mother plastered it.
The inside walls are white;
My Mother made them white;
The floor is smooth;
My Mother made it smooth,
For me to live there.

"In My Mother's House" is an excerpt from the book *In My Mother's House*.

In my Mother's house
There is a fireplace;
The fireplace holds the fire.
On dark nights the fire is bright;
On cold nights the fire is warm.
The fire is always there,
To help me see,
To keep me warm.

In my Mother's house
There are the grinding stones:
The big, flat holding stone,
The small rubbing stone;
The grinding stones,
My Mother's grinding stones.

On the floor
Beside her stones
My Mother kneels,
And with her hands
She grinds the corn;
Yellow corn and blue corn
My Mother grinds
For me to eat.

Red chili and meat and melons
and yellow cornmeal
I have to eat.

Apricots and peaches
And little red plums
I have to eat.
Big round tortillas
And brown frijoles
I have to eat.
I eat them;
I like them.

In my Mother's house
All day
I play and work;
All night
I sleep.

The walls come close around me
In a good way.
I can see them;
I can feel them;
I live with them.

This house is good to me,
It keeps me;
I like it,
My Mother's house.

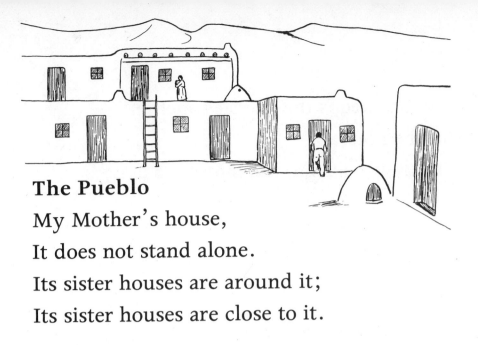

The Pueblo

My Mother's house,
It does not stand alone.
Its sister houses are around it;
Its sister houses are close to it.

Like holding hands,
The houses stand close together
Around the plaza.
Houses are the stay-in places,
But the plaza
Is the live-in place
For all the people.

In the plaza the people work;
In the plaza the people play
And sing and dance
And make ready for feasting.
It is the place
For all the people.

The plaza keeps the people together,
And the houses
With their backs to the mountains,
Stand facing the plaza
And shut it in.

My Mother's house,
It does not stand alone;
Its sister houses
Are all around it.

People
We are the people
Living together,
All of us together.

We live here
In the houses,
In the plaza
Together.

When it is dark
All of us are sleeping.

When it is day
We are working,
Always
Together.

It is good to stand close
Like our houses.

The Council
The Wise Ones
Are our Fathers.
They tell us what to do;
They keep us;
Like the plaza,
They keep us
Together.

Sharing Time

1. How does the child feel about his house?

2. What did his mother and father do to make the house?

3. What does the child have to eat?

4. What keeps his people together?

5. How is his house different from yours? How is it like yours?

Us Two
A. A. Milne

Wherever I am, there's always Pooh,
There's always Pooh and Me.
Whatever I do, he wants to do,
"Where are you going to-day?" says Pooh:
"Well, that's very odd 'cos I was too.
Let's go together," says Pooh, says he.
"Let's go together," says Pooh.

"What's twice eleven?" I said to Pooh.
("Twice what?" said Pooh to Me.)
"I *think* it ought to be twenty-two."
"Just what I think myself," said Pooh.
"It wasn't an easy sum to do,
But that's what it is," said Pooh, said he.
"That's what it is," said Pooh.

"Let's look for dragons," I said to Pooh.
"Yes, let's," said Pooh to Me.
We crossed the river and found a few—
"Yes, those are dragons all right," said Pooh.
"As soon as I saw their beaks I knew.
That's what they are," said Pooh, said he.
"That's what they are," said Pooh.

"Let's frighten the dragons," I said to Pooh.
"That's right," said Pooh to Me.
"*I'm* not afraid," I said to Pooh,
And I held his paw and I shouted "Shoo!
Silly old dragons!"—and off they flew.
"I wasn't afraid," said Pooh, said he,
"I'm *never* afraid with you."

So wherever I am, there's always Pooh,
There's always Pooh and Me.
"What would I do?" I said to Pooh,
"If it wasn't for you," and Pooh said: "True,
It isn't much fun for One, but Two
Can stick together," says Pooh, says he.
"That's how it is," says Pooh.

Rumpelstiltzkin

Retold by Andrew Lang

There was once upon a time a poor miller who had a very beautiful daughter. Now, it happened one day that he had an audience with the king, and in order to appear a person of some importance he told him that he had a daughter who could spin straw into gold. "Now that is a talent worth having," said the king to the miller. "If your daughter is as clever as you say, bring her to my palace tomorrow."

When the girl came he led her into a room full of straw, gave her a spinning wheel and spindle, and said, "Now set to work and spin all night till early dawn, and if by that

126

time you have not spun the straw into gold
you shall die."

Then he closed the door behind him and
left her alone inside.

So the poor miller's daughter sat down
and did not know what in the world she was
to do. She had not the least idea of how to
spin straw into gold and at last became so
miserable that she began to cry. Suddenly the
door opened, and in stepped a tiny little man
who said:

"Good evening, Miss Miller-maid. Why
are you crying so bitterly?"

"Oh," answered the girl, "I have to spin
straw into gold and I haven't a notion how it
is done."

"What will you give me if I spin it for you?" asked the manikin.

"My necklace," replied the girl.

The little man took the necklace, sat himself down at the wheel, and whir, whir, whir, the wheel went round three times, and the bobbin was full. Then he put on another, and whir, whir, whir, the wheel went round three times, and the second too was full. And so it went on till the morning, when all the straw was spun away, and all the bobbins were full of gold.

As soon as the sun rose the king came, and when he perceived the gold he was astonished and delighted, but he was only more greedy than ever for the precious metal. He had the miller's daughter put into another

room full of straw, much bigger than the first, and bade her, if she valued her life, spin it all into gold before the following morning.

The girl did not know what to do and began to cry. Then the door opened as before, and the tiny little man appeared, and said:

"What will you give me if I spin the straw into gold for you?"

"The ring from my finger," said the girl.

The manikin took the ring, and whir! Round went the spinning wheel again, and when morning broke he had spun all the straw into glittering gold. The king was pleased beyond measure at the sight, but he was still not satisfied, and he had the miller's daughter brought into a yet bigger room full of straw.

"You must spin all this away in the night," he said, "but if you succeed this time you shall become my wife." She's only a miller's daughter, he thought, but I could not find a richer wife if I were to search the whole world over.

When the girl was alone the little man appeared for the third time, and said, "What will you give me if I spin the straw for you once again?"

"I've nothing more to give," answered the girl.

"Then promise me when you are queen to give me your first child."

Who knows what may happen before that, thought the miller's daughter, and besides, she saw no other way out of it. So she promised the manikin what he demanded, and he set to work once more and spun the straw into gold. When the king came in the morning and found everything as he had desired, he straightway made her his wife, and the miller's daughter became a queen.

When a year had passed a beautiful son
was born to her, and she thought no more of
the little man, till all of a sudden one day,
he stepped into her room, and said, "Now
give me what you promised." The queen was
in a great state, and offered the little man all
the riches in her kingdom if he would only
leave her the child.

But the manikin said, "No, a living
creature is dearer to me than all the treasures
in the world." Then the queen began to cry
and sob so bitterly that the little man was
sorry for her, and said:

"I'll give you three days to guess my
name, and if you find it out in that time you
may keep your child."

Then the queen pondered the whole night
over all of the names she had ever heard and
sent a messenger to scour the land and to
pick up far and near any names he should
come across. When the little man arrived on
the following day she began with Kasper,
Melchior, Belshazzar, and all the other names
she knew, but at each one the manikin called
out, "That's not my name." The next day she
sent to inquire the names of all the people in
the neighborhood and had a long list of the
most uncommon and extraordinary for the
little man.

"Is your name, perhaps, Sheepshanks,
Cruickshanks, Spindleshanks?"

But he always replied, "That is not my
name."

On the third day the messenger returned
and announced:

"I have not been able to find any new
names; but as I came upon a high hill round
the corner of the wood, where the foxes and

hares bid each other good night, I saw a little house, and in front of the house burned a fire, and round the fire sprang the most grotesque little man, hopping on one leg, and crying:

> '*Tomorrow I brew, today I bake,*
> *And then the child away I'll take;*
> *For little deems my royal dame*
> *That Rumpelstiltzkin is my name!*' "

Imagine the queen's delight at hearing the name, and when the little man stepped in shortly afterward and asked, "Now, my Lady Queen, what is my name?" she asked first:

"Is your name Conrad?"

"No."

"Is your name Harry?"

"No."

"Is your name, perhaps, Rumpelstiltzkin?"

"Some demon has told you that! Some demon has told you that!" screamed the little man, and in his rage he drove his right foot so far into the ground that it sank in up to his waist. Then in a passion he seized the left foot with both hands and tore himself in two.

Sharing Time

1. How did Rumpelstiltzkin help the miller's daughter?

2. What payment did Rumpelstiltzkin get?

3. How did the queen learn Rumpelstiltzkin's name?

4. What makes this a good story?

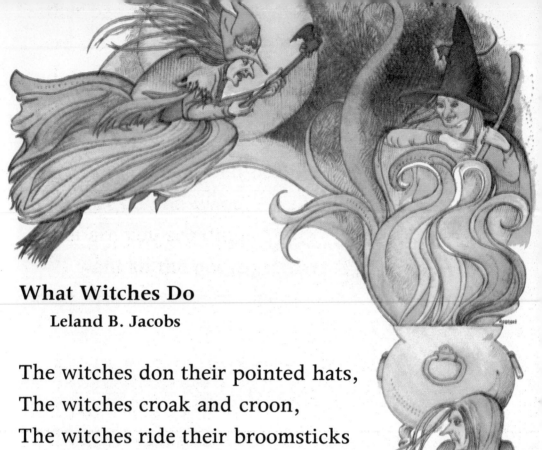

What Witches Do

Leland B. Jacobs

The witches don their pointed hats,
The witches croak and croon,
The witches ride their broomsticks
Away beyond the moon.

The witches don their flowing cloaks,
The witches stir their brew,
The witches chant their magic spells
All the dark hours through.

The witches stroke their big black cats,
They comb their locks of gray,
Yet when the first faint daylight comes,
The witches hide away.

Lazy Jack

Retold by Veronica S. Hutchinson

Once upon a time there was a boy whose name was Jack, and he and his mother lived in a little house on a common.

They were very poor, and the mother earned her living by spinning. Jack, however, was so lazy that he would do nothing but bask in the sun in the hot weather and sit by the corner of the hearth in the winter-time. Because of this, they called him "Lazy Jack."

His mother could not get him to do anything for her; so at last she told him that if he did not begin to work for his porridge he would have to go out into the world and earn his living as he could.

This roused Jack, and he went out and hired himself for the next day to a neighboring farmer for a penny. But as he was on his way home, never having had any money before, he lost it in passing over a brook.

When he reached home and his mother found out what had happened, she said: "You stupid boy, you should have put it in your pocket."

"I'll do so another time," replied Jack.

Well, the next day Jack went out again and hired himself to a cow keeper, who gave him a jar of milk for his day's work. Jack took the jar and put it into the large pocket of his jacket, spilling it all long before he reached home.

"Dear me," said his mother; "you should have carried it on your head."

"I'll do so another time," said Jack.

So the following day Jack hired himself to a farmer, who agreed to give him a cream cheese for his services. In the evening Jack took the cream cheese and went home with it on his head.

By the time he reached home, the cheese was all spoilt, part of it being lost and part dripping down over his face.

"You stupid lad," said his mother, "you should have carried it carefully in your hands."

"I'll do so another time," replied Jack.

Now the next day Jack went out and hired himself to a baker, who would give him nothing for his work but a large tom-cat. Jack took the cat and began carrying it very carefully in his hands, but in a short time pussy scratched him so much that he was compelled to let it go.

When he reached home, his mother said to him: "You silly fellow, you should have tied it with a string and dragged it along after you."

"I'll do so another time," said Jack.

So on the following day Jack hired himself to a butcher who rewarded him by the handsome present of a shoulder of mutton.

Jack took the mutton, tied it to a string, and trailed it along after him in the dirt, so that by the time he reached home the meat was completely spoilt.

By this time his mother was quite out of patience with him, for the next day was Sunday, and she was obliged to do with cabbage for her dinner.

"You heedless boy," said she to her son; "you should have carried it on your shoulder."

"I'll do so another time," replied Jack.

Well, on Monday Jack went once more and hired himself to a cattle-keeper, who gave him a donkey for his trouble. Now, though Jack was strong, he found it hard to hoist the donkey on his shoulders, but at last he did it, and began walking home slowly with his prize.

It so happened that on his way home he passed a house where a rich man lived with his only daughter, a beautiful girl, but who had never laughed in her life, and so her father said that the man who could make her laugh could marry her.

Now this young lady happened to be looking out of the window when Jack was passing by with the donkey on his shoulders. The poor beast with its legs sticking up in the air was kicking hard and heehawing with all its might.

Well, the sight was so comical that she burst out into a great fit of laughter. Her father was overjoyed and kept his promise by marrying her to Jack, who was then made a rich gentleman.

They lived in a great house and Jack's mother lived with them in great happiness for the rest of her days.

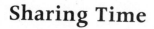

1. Why did Lazy Jack get to marry the girl?

2. What happened each time Jack followed his mother's directions?

3. How can you tell this is an old story?

4. What makes this story easy to tell?

The Best Game the Fairies Play

Rose Fyleman

The best game the fairies play,
The best game of all,
Is sliding down steeples—
(You know they're very tall.)
You fly to the weathercock,
And when you hear it crow
You fold your wings and clutch your things
And then let go!

They have a million other games—
Cloud-catching's one,
And mud-mixing after rain
Is heaps and heaps of fun;
But when you go and stay with them
Never mind the rest,
Take my advice—they're very nice,
But steeple-sliding's best!

Sleeping Beauty
Jakob and Wilhelm Grimm

A long time ago there lived a King and Queen, who said every day, "If only we had a child!" But for a long time they had none.

One day, as the Queen was bathing, a frog crept out of the water on to the land and said to her, "Your wish shall be fulfilled. Before a year has passed you shall bring a daughter into the world."

The frog's words came true. The Queen had a little girl who was so beautiful that the King could not contain himself for joy. He prepared a great feast and invited all his relations and friends and neighbors. He invited the fairies, too, in order that they might be kind and good to the child. There were thirteen of them in the kingdom, but as the King had only twelve golden plates for them to eat from, one of the fairies had to be left out.

The feast was held with all splendor, and when it came to an end, each of the fairies presented the child with a magic gift. One fairy gave her virtue, another beauty, a third riches, and so on, with everything in the world that she could wish for.

When eleven of the fairies had said their say, the thirteenth suddenly appeared. She wanted to show her spite for not having been invited. Without greeting anyone, or even glancing at anyone, she called out in a loud voice, "When she is fifteen years old, the Princess shall prick herself with a spindle and shall fall down dead."

Then without another word she turned and left the hall.

Everyone was terror-stricken, but the twelfth fairy, whose wish was still not spoken, stepped forward. She could not take away the curse, but could only soften it, so she said, "Your daughter shall not die, but shall fall into a deep sleep lasting a hundred years."

The King was so anxious to guard his dear child from this misfortune that he sent out a command that all the spindles in the whole kingdom should be burned.

All the promises of the fairies came true.
The Princess grew up so beautiful, modest,
kind, and clever that everybody who saw her
could not but love her.

Now it happened that on the very day
when she was fifteen years old the King and
Queen were away from home, and the
Princess was left quite alone in the castle.

She wandered about over the whole place, looking at rooms and halls as she pleased, and at last she came to an old tower. She went up a narrow, winding staircase and reached a little door. A rusty key was sticking in the lock, and when she turned it the door flew open.

In a little room sat an old woman with a spindle, busily spinning her flax. This old woman was so deaf that she had never heard the King's command that all spindles should be destroyed.

"Good day, Granny," said the Princess, "what are you doing?"

"I am spinning," said the old woman, and nodded her head.

"What is the thing that whirls round so merrily?" asked the Princess, and she took the spindle and tried to spin, too.

But she had scarcely touched the spindle when it pricked her finger. At that moment she fell upon the bed which was standing near, and lay still in a deep sleep.

The King and Queen, who had just come home and had stepped into the hall, fell asleep, too, and all their courtiers with them. The horses fell asleep in the stable, the dogs in the yard, the doves on the roof, the flies on the wall. Yes, even the fire on the hearth grew still and went to sleep, and the meat that was roasting stopped crackling. The kitchen maid, who sat with a fowl before her, ready to pluck its feathers, fell asleep. The cook, too, who was pulling the kitchen boy's hair because he had made a mistake, let him go and both fell asleep. The wind dropped, and on the trees in front of the castle not a leaf stirred.

Round the castle a hedge of brier roses began to grow up. Every year it grew higher, till at last nothing could be seen of the castle.

There was a legend in the land about the lovely Sleeping Beauty, as the King's daughter was called, and from time to time Princes came and tried to force a way through the hedge into the castle. But they found it impossible, for the thorns, as though they had hands, held them fast, and the Princes remained caught in them without being able to free themselves, and so died.

After many, many years a Prince came
again to the country and heard an old man
tell of the castle which stood behind the brier
hedge, in which a most beautiful maiden
called Sleeping Beauty had been asleep for the

last hundred years, and with her slept the King and Queen, and all their courtiers. He knew, also, from his grandfather, that many Princes had already come and sought to pierce through the brier hedge, and had been caught in it and died.

Then the young Prince said, "I am not afraid. I must go and see this Sleeping Beauty."

The good old man did all in his power to persuade him not to go, but the Prince would not listen to his words.

Now the hundred years were just ended. When the Prince approached the brier hedge it was covered with beautiful large blossoms. The shrubs made way for him of their own accord and let him pass unharmed, and then closed up again into a hedge.

In the courtyard he saw the horses and dogs lying asleep. On the roof sat the doves with their heads under their wings. When he went into the house the flies were asleep on the walls. Near the throne lay the King and Queen. In the kitchen the cook still had his hand raised as though to strike the kitchen boy, and the maid sat with the black fowl before her ready to pluck its feathers.

He went on farther. All was so still that he could hear his own breathing. At last he reached the tower, and opened the door into the little room where the Princess was asleep. There she lay, looking so beautiful that he could not take his eyes off her. He bent down and gave her a kiss. As he touched her, Sleeping Beauty opened her eyes and smiled at him.

Then they went down together. The King and the Queen and all the courtiers woke up, and looked at each other with astonished eyes. The horses in the stable stood up and shook themselves. The hounds leaped about and wagged their tails. The doves on the roof lifted their heads from under their wings, looked around, and flew into the fields. The flies on the walls began to crawl again. The fire in the kitchen roused itself and blazed up and cooked the food. The meat began to crackle, and the cook woke up and boxed the kitchen boy's ears so that he screamed aloud, while the maid finished plucking the fowl.

Then the Prince and Sleeping Beauty were married with all splendor, and they lived happily all their lives.

Sharing Time

1. Why was a curse put on the Princess?

2. How did the King try to protect his daughter?

3. What happened on the Princess' fifteenth birthday?

4. What made the Princess wake up?

5. How do you know this story is make-believe?

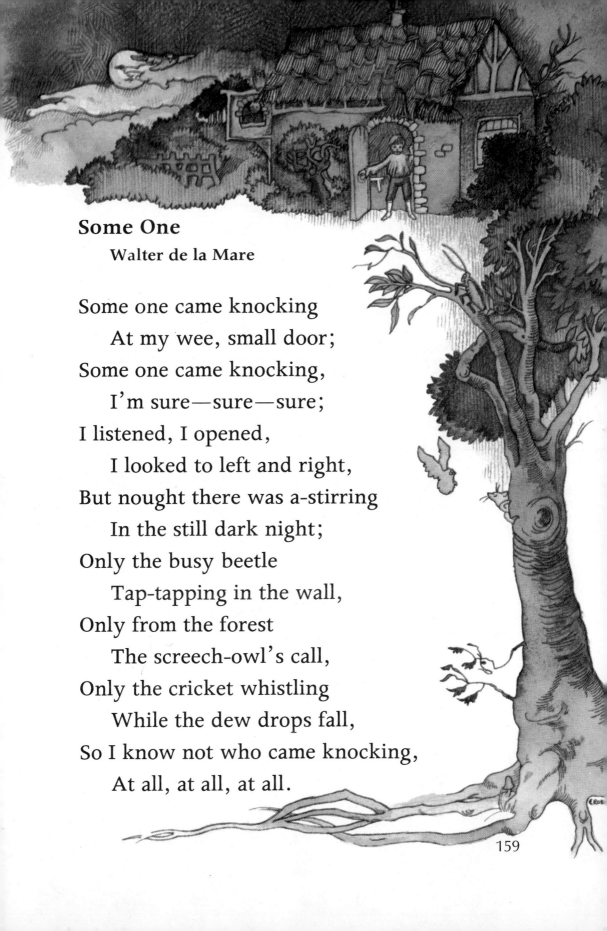

Some One

Walter de la Mare

Some one came knocking
　At my wee, small door;
Some one came knocking,
　I'm sure—sure—sure;
I listened, I opened,
　I looked to left and right,
But nought there was a-stirring
　In the still dark night;
Only the busy beetle
　Tap-tapping in the wall,
Only from the forest
　The screech-owl's call,
Only the cricket whistling
　While the dew drops fall,
So I know not who came knocking,
　At all, at all, at all.

159

The Story of Ferdinand
Munro Leaf

Once upon a time in Spain there was a little bull and his name was Ferdinand. All the other little bulls he lived with would run and jump and butt their heads together, but not Ferdinand. He liked to sit just quietly and smell the flowers.

He had a favorite spot out in the pasture under a cork tree. It was his favorite tree and he would sit in its shade all day and smell the flowers.

Sometimes his mother, who was a cow, would worry about him. She was afraid he would be lonesome all by himself.

"Why don't you run and play with the other little bulls and skip and butt your head?" she would say.

But Ferdinand would shake his head.
"I like it better here where I can sit just
quietly and smell the flowers."

His mother saw that he was not lonesome,
and because she was an understanding
mother, even though she was a cow, she let
him just sit there and be happy.

As the years went by Ferdinand grew and
grew until he was very big and strong.

All the other bulls who had grown up
with him in the same pasture would fight
each other all day. They would butt each
other and stick each other with their horns.
What they wanted most of all was to be
picked to fight at the bull fights in Madrid.

But not Ferdinand—he still liked to sit
just quietly under the cork tree and smell the
flowers.

One day five men came in very funny hats
to pick the biggest, fastest, roughest bull to
fight in the bull fights in Madrid.

All the other bulls ran around snorting
and butting, leaping and jumping so the men
would think that they were very very strong
and fierce and pick them.

Ferdinand knew that they wouldn't pick
him and he didn't care. So he went out to his
favorite cork tree to sit down. He didn't look
where he was sitting and instead of sitting on
the nice cool grass in the shade he sat on a
bumble bee.

Well, if you were a bumble bee and a bull sat on you what would you do?

You would sting him. And that is just what this bee did to Ferdinand.

Wow! Did it hurt! Ferdinand jumped up with a snort. He ran around puffing and snorting, butting and pawing the ground as if he were crazy.

The five men saw him and they all shouted with joy. Here was the largest and fiercest bull of all. Just the one for the bull fights in Madrid!

So they took him away for the bull fight day in a cart.

What a day it was! Flags were flying, bands were playing . . . and all the lovely ladies had flowers in their hair.

They had a parade into the bull ring.

First came the Banderilleros with long sharp pins with ribbons on them to stick in the bull and make him mad.

Next came the Picadores who rode skinny horses and they had long spears to stick in the bull and make him madder.

Then came the Matador, the proudest of all—he thought he was very handsome, and bowed to the ladies. He had a red cape and a sword and was supposed to stick the bull last of all.

Then came the bull, and you know who that was don't you?

Ferdinand

They called him Ferdinand the Fierce and all the Banderilleros were afraid of him and the Picadores were afraid of him and the Matador was scared stiff.

Ferdinand ran to the middle of the ring and everyone shouted and clapped because they thought he was going to fight fiercely and butt and snort and stick his horns around.

But not Ferdinand. When he got to the middle of the ring he saw the flowers in all the lovely ladies' hair and he just sat down quietly and smelled.

He wouldn't fight and be fierce no matter what they did. He just sat and smelled. And the Banderilleros were mad and the Picadores were madder and the Matador was so mad he cried because he couldn't show off with his cape and sword.

So they had to take Ferdinand home.

And for all I know he is sitting there still, under his favorite cork tree, smelling the flowers just quietly.

He is very happy.

Sharing Time

1. How was Ferdinand different from the other bulls?

2. Why did the men choose Ferdinand to fight in Madrid?

3. What happened at the bull fight?

4. What makes this story funny?

Dandelion

Don Freeman

On a sunny Saturday morning Dandelion
woke up, stretched and yawned, and jumped
out of bed.

After doing his daily exercises Dandelion
looked out of the window, blinked his eyes,
and said, "I wonder if the mail has come?"
He put on his sweater and went outside to the
mailbox. There was a letter, and it was written
in fancy gold ink!

170

Dear Dandelion:
     You are invited
to my tea-and-taffy party
on Saturday afternoon at
half-past three.
     Come as you are.
          Sincerely,
               Jennifer Giraffe

Dandelion was very excited. "Why, that's today!" he said. "It's a good thing I planned to get a haircut!"

As soon as he had washed and dried the breakfast dishes and made his bed nice and neat, he ran down the street to the barbershop. Lou Kangaroo had a chair waiting for him. First he trimmed Dandelion's hair, and then gave him a shampoo. Dandelion thought he should have a manicure too.

When Lou Kangaroo had finished Dandelion looked a bit foolish. His mane was frizzy and fuzzy and completely unrulish.

"Maybe a wave would help," Lou suggested, showing him a picture in the latest fashion magazine for lions. Dandelion agreed.

This was exactly what he needed. So Lou went about curling his mane.

He looked magnificent!

But now Dandelion thought he really should wear something more elegant than a sweater to the party.

"This jacket is the very newest style," said Theodore the Tailor, "and it just fits you. All you need now is a cap and a cane. Happy Crane will be glad to help you."

What a dapper dandy he had suddenly become!

"It's nearly half-past three!" said Dandelion. "I've just time to get something for my hostess!"

A bouquet of dandelions would be perfect.

He knew this tall door very well, having
been here many times before. He rang the bell.

When Jennifer Giraffe opened the door
she looked very surprised. "Yes?" she said.
"What can I do for you?"

"Why, I've come to your party," he
answered.

"Oh, I'm sorry, sir, but you are not
anyone I know!" said Miss Giraffe. "You
must have come to the wrong address."

And with this she closed the door right in
poor Dandelion's face!

"I'm Dandelion!" he roared. "You've
made a mighty mistake!" But there was no

use knocking. The door stayed tight shut.

Dandelion began walking back and forth. Back and forth, up and down the long block he paced. And as he paced, the sky grew dark. Then a sudden gust of wind sprang up and blew away his beautiful bouquet, and his snappy cap flew off!

To make matters worse, it began to rain in torrents. Dandelion dropped his cane and stood under a weeping willow tree. But the rain poured down through the branches. Dandelion was soon soaking wet and his curls came unfurled.

He took off his jacket and hung it on a willow branch. Luckily he had kept on his sweater.

At last the rain stopped and the warm sunshine came beaming down.

Dandelion decided to sit on Jennifer Giraffe's front steps until his mane was dry. While he sat there waiting he spied three dandelion flowers under the bottom step where they had been protected from the wind and the rain. He picked the dandelions and said, "I think I will try again." And he rang the bell.

"Well, well! If it isn't our friend Dandelion at last!" said Jennifer Giraffe. "We've been waiting for you for the past hour. I do hope you weren't caught in that awful cloudburst!"

Everyone at the party greeted him heartily.

Later on when all her guests were enjoying tea and taffy, Jennifer Giraffe told Dandelion about the silly-looking lion who had come to the door earlier. Dandelion almost spilled his cup of tea as he reared back and laughed uproariously, "Oh, that was me! I was that silly-looking lion!"

Miss Giraffe was so flustered she got herself all tangled up in her long pearl necklace. "I do apologize for having closed the door on you!" she said blushing. "I promise never to do such a thing again!"

"And I promise you I will never again try to turn myself into a stylish dandy," said Dandelion as he sipped his tea. "From now on I'll always be just plain me!"

Sharing Time

1. What did Dandelion do to
   get ready for the party?

2. How do you think Dandelion
   felt when Jennifer Giraffe
   did not know him?

3. What lesson did Dandelion
   learn?

4. Do you think Dandelion's
   lesson is an important one?
   Why or why not?

The Monkeys and the Crocodile

Laura E. Richards

Five little monkeys
   Swinging from a tree;
Teasing Uncle Crocodile,
   Merry as can be.
Swinging high, swinging low,
   Swinging left and right:
"Dear Uncle Crocodile,
   Come and take a bite!"

Five little monkeys
   Swinging in the air;
Heads up, tails up,
   Little do they care.
Swinging up, swinging down,
   Swinging far and near:
"Poor Uncle Crocodile,
   Aren't you hungry, dear?"

Four little monkeys
    Sitting in the tree;
Heads down, tails down,
    Dreary as can be.
Weeping loud, weeping low,
    Crying to each other:
"Wicked Uncle Crocodile,
    To gobble up our brother!"

The Poppy Seed Cakes

Margery Clark

Once upon a time there was a little boy and his name was Andrewshek. His mother and his father brought him from the old country when he was a tiny baby.

Andrewshek had an Auntie Katushka and she came from the old country, too, on Andrewshek's fourth birthday.

Andrewshek's Auntie Katushka came on a large boat. She brought with her a huge bag filled with presents for Andrewshek and his father and his mother. In the huge bag were a fine feather bed and a bright shawl and five pounds of poppy seeds.

The fine feather bed was made from the feathers of her old green goose at home. It was to keep Andrewshek warm when he took a nap.

 The bright shawl was for Andrewshek's Auntie Katushka to wear when she went to market.

The five pounds of poppy seeds were to sprinkle on little cakes which Andrewshek's Auntie Katushka made every Saturday for Andrewshek.

One lovely Saturday morning Andrewshek's Auntie Katushka took some butter and some sugar and some flour and some milk and

seven eggs and she rolled out some nice little
cakes. Then she sprinkled each cake with
some of the poppy seeds which she had
brought from the old country.

While the nice little cakes were baking,
she spread out the fine feather bed on top of
the big bed, for Andrewshek to take his nap.
Andrewshek did not like to take a nap.

Andrewshek loved to bounce up and down and up and down on his fine feather bed.

Andrewshek's Auntie Katushka took the nice little cakes out of the oven and put them on the table to cool; then she put on her bright shawl to go to market. "Andrewshek," she said, "please watch these cakes while you rest on your fine feather bed. Be sure that the kitten and the dog do not go near them."

"Yes, indeed! I will watch the nice little cakes," said Andrewshek. "And I will be sure that the kitten and the dog do not touch them." But all Andrewshek really did was to bounce up and down and up and down on the fine feather bed.

"Andrewshek!" said Andrewshek's Auntie Katushka, "how can you watch the poppy seed cakes when all you do is to bounce up and down and up and down on the fine feather bed?" Then Andrewshek's Auntie Katushka, in her bright shawl, hurried off to market.

But Andrewshek kept bouncing up and down and up and down on the fine feather bed and paid no attention to the little cakes sprinkled with poppy seeds.

Just as Andrewshek was bouncing up in the air for the ninth time, he heard a queer noise that sounded like "Hs-s-s-s-sss," at the front door of his house.

"Oh, what a queer noise!" cried Andrewshek. He jumped down off the fine feather bed and opened the front door. There stood a great green goose as big as Andrewshek himself. The goose was very cross and was scolding as fast as he could. He was wagging his head and was opening and closing his long red beak.

"What do you want?" said Andrewshek. "What are you scolding about?"

"I want all the goose feathers from your

fine feather bed," quacked the big green goose. "They are mine."

"They are not yours," said Andrewshek. "My Auntie Katushka brought them with her from the old country in a huge bag."

"They are mine," quacked the big green goose. He waddled over to the fine feather bed and tugged at it with his long red beak.

"Stop, Green Goose!" said Andrewshek, "and I will give you one of Auntie Katushka's poppy seed cakes."

"A poppy seed cake!" the green goose quacked in delight. "I love nice little poppy seed cakes! Give me one and you shall have your feather bed."

But one poppy seed cake could not satisfy the greedy green goose.

"Give me another!" Andrewshek gave the green goose another poppy seed cake.

"Give me another!" the big green goose hissed and frightened Andrewshek nearly out of his wits.

Andrewshek gave him another and another and another till all the poppy seed cakes were gone.

Just as the last poppy seed cake disappeared down the long neck of the green goose, Andrewshek's Auntie Katushka appeared at the door, in her bright shawl. "Boo! hoo!" cried Andrewshek. "See! That naughty green goose has eaten all the poppy seed cakes."

"What? All my nice little poppy seed cakes?" cried Andrewshek's Auntie Katushka. "The naughty goose!"

The greedy goose tugged at the fine feather bed again with his long red beak and started to drag it to the door. Andrewshek's Auntie Katushka ran after the green goose and just then there was a dreadful explosion. The greedy goose who had stuffed himself with poppy seed cakes had burst and his feathers flew all over the room.

"Well! well!" said Andrewshek's Auntie Katushka, as she gathered up the pieces of the big green goose. "We soon shall have two fine feather pillows for your fine feather bed."

Sharing Time

1. What happened to the green goose?

2. Why did Andrewshek give the goose the poppy seed cakes?

3. Why did Auntie Katushka bring the things she did from the old country?

4. What three things would you take with you if you moved to a new country?

5. Why would you like Andrewshek for a playmate?

The Reason for the Pelican

John Ciardi

The reason for the pelican
Is difficult to see:
His beak is clearly larger
Than there's any need to be.

It's not to bail a boat with—
He doesn't own a boat.
Yet everywhere he takes himself
He has that beak to tote.

It's not to keep his wife in—
His wife has got one, too.
It's not a scoop for eating soup.
It's not an extra shoe.

It isn't quite for anything.
And yet you realize
It's really quite a splendid beak
In quite a splendid size.

Frederick

Leo Lionni

All along the meadow where the cows grazed and the horses ran, there was an old stone wall. In that wall, not far from the barn and the granary, a chatty family of field mice had their home. But the farmers had moved away, the barn was abandoned, and the granary stood empty. And since winter was not far off, the little mice began to gather corn and nuts and wheat and straw. They all worked day and night. All—except Frederick.

"Frederick, why don't you work?" they asked.

"I *do* work," said Frederick.

"I gather sun rays for the cold dark winter days."

And when they saw Frederick sitting there, staring at the meadow, they said, "And now, Frederick?"

"I gather colors," answered Frederick simply. "For winter is gray."

And once Frederick seemed half asleep. "Are you dreaming, Frederick?" they asked reproachfully.

But Frederick said, "Oh no, I am gathering words. For the winter days are long and many, and we'll run out of things to say."

The winter days came, and when the first snow fell the five little field mice took to their hideout in the stones. In the beginning there was lots to eat, and the mice told stories of foolish foxes and silly cats. They were a happy family.

But little by little they had nibbled up most of the nuts and berries, the straw was gone, and the corn was only a memory. It was cold in the wall and no one felt like chatting.

Then they remembered what Frederick had said about sun rays and colors and words.

"What about *your* supplies, Frederick?" they asked.

"Close your eyes," said Frederick, as he climbed on a big stone. "Now I send you the rays of the sun. Do you feel how their golden glow . . ." And as Frederick spoke of the sun the four little mice began to feel warmer. Was it Frederick's voice? Was it magic?

"And how about the colors, Frederick?" they asked anxiously.

"Close your eyes again," Frederick said. And when he told them of the blue periwinkles, the red poppies in the yellow wheat, and the green leaves of the berry bush, they saw the colors as clearly as if they had been painted in their minds.

"And the words, Frederick?"

Frederick cleared his throat, waited a
moment, and then, as if from a stage, he said:

"Who scatters snowflakes? Who melts the
   ice?
Who spoils the weather? Who makes it nice?
Who grows the four-leaf clovers in June?
Who dims the daylight? Who lights the
   moon?

Four little field mice who live in the sky.
Four little field mice . . . like you and I.

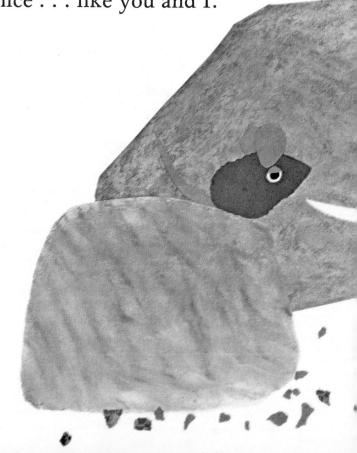

One is the Springmouse who turns on the
    showers.
Then comes the Summer who paints in the
    flowers.
The Fallmouse is next with walnuts and
    wheat.
And Winter is last . . . with little cold feet.

Aren't we lucky the seasons are four?
Think of a year with one less . . . or one more!"

When Frederick had finished, they all applauded. "But Frederick," they said, "you are a poet!"

Frederick blushed, took a bow, and said shyly, "I know it."

Sharing Time

1. How was Frederick's work different from that of the other mice?

2. What three things did Frederick gather?

3. What other supplies could Frederick have stored?

4. What do you think Frederick was trying to tell the other mice?

5. What do you do in summer to store up things for winter?

Do You See What I See?
Helen Borten

I see lines and shapes and colors everywhere around me.

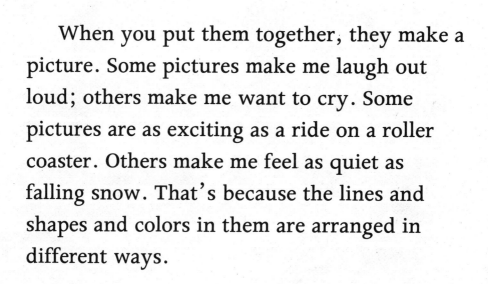

This is a line.

This is a shape.

This is a color.

When you put them together, they make a picture. Some pictures make me laugh out loud; others make me want to cry. Some pictures are as exciting as a ride on a roller coaster. Others make me feel as quiet as falling snow. That's because the lines and shapes and colors in them are arranged in different ways.

Up and down lines pull me up, up, up with them, until I feel as tall as a steeple and as taut as a stretched rubber band. I think of lofty things—giant redwood trees, a lighthouse rising above the sea, a rocket soaring high into the sky, noble kings in flowing robes.

Flat lines, side by side, make me feel calm and peaceful. I think of ploughed fields stretching across the countryside.

And I remember floating like a log on the smooth surface of a lake.

Slanted lines can rush me downward on
a slide or sliding pond. Or they can soar me
high on a pair of skis. For slanted lines are
like a seesaw—sometimes they go up, and
sometimes they come down.

Lines can bend like rows of wheat when
a soft breeze blows. They can bend in other
ways too. Lines that bend in a zigzag way
seem to crackle with excitement. They make
me think of thunder storms and jagged
mountain peaks. I see the huge jaws of a
crocodile, wide open and bristling with
jagged teeth, ready to snap shut.

Lines can bend in a curved way, too. A curved line is like a swan, full of beauty and grace. It can rise and curl slowly, as lazy as smoke. It can twirl like a dancer, or flow and swirl like water in a stream full of speckled fish.

Lines can be as thin and delicate as a spider web, or as heavy and black as the bars of a lion's cage.

Lines can be as ragged as a barbed wire fence, or as smooth as the thread in mother's sewing box.

I see lines everywhere around me—skinny ones and fat ones, timid ones and bold ones, wiggly ones and straight ones, hard ones and soft ones, shaggy ones and smooth ones, fast ones and slow ones.

Wherever I look I see lines making patterns of beauty. Can you see them, too?

If you bend a line far enough, it becomes
a circle. A circle is a "shape"—a merry,
cherry shape. It can roll like a ball, or float
like a bubble, or turn like a ferris wheel.
It can be as calm as the moon, as gentle as a
curled-up kitten, or as fat and jolly as
Santa Claus.

Some circles can even make you giggle!
Have you ever watched a frog about to sing?
He blows his throat up like a balloon and
out comes "chugaroom, chugaroom."

When four straight lines meet like this
the shape they make is called a "square."
Now, a square can never roll like a ball. But
it can stand as steady as your building blocks.
Squares have a neat, careful look, like a
window screen or a checkerboard.

A high building is like a square that
has been stretched and stretched until it is
tall and skinny. That kind of shape is called
a "rectangle." A big city looks like a maze of
squares and rectangles piled on top of each
other, with little ones inside of big ones.

When three straight lines meet like this △
the shape they make is called a
"triangle." It seems to me
that triangles push
and pull in a
hard, stiff
way.
And
sometimes
they force me to
look where they are
pointing, like an arrowhead on a sign.
Here are some things that look like triangles.

One day I saw six jet planes flying by.
They looked like six silver triangles flying in
a row. Did you ever see a sly, red fox? His
pointed face is almost as sharp as a triangle.

I see shapes everywhere around me—
skinny ones and fat ones, smooth ones and
lumpy ones, squeezed-in ones and pushed-out
ones.

You have a shape. And so does your dog
and your toys and the flowers and butterflies
in your garden. You see, everything in the
world has a shape!

Everything has a color, too. Different colors make us feel different ways, just as lines and shapes do. Red is hot like a crackling fire, and blue is cold like a mountain stream.

Yellow is warm like the sun's rays, and green is as cool as a crisp leaf of lettuce.

Colors can be pale and timid as a mouse—
or dark and mysterious as the night.

Some colors are as dull as the sky on a
rainy day when everything is dripping and
gray. Others are so bright they make me
blink. Bright colors clang for attention like a
fire engine. They are as exciting as city lights
flashing on and off after dark.

Sometimes colors that are next to each other stand out as clear and bold as the stripes on a zebra. But sometimes you can hardly tell where one color stops and another color begins. Way, way out where the ocean meets the sky is like that. I see colors everywhere around me—warm ones and cool ones, bright ones and dull ones, clear ones and muddy ones, gay ones and sad ones.

I see the world as a great big painting, full of lines and shapes and colors, to look at and enjoy.

Do you see
What I see?

Sharing Time

1. What are the three main
   ideas explained in the story?

2. Choose one of the ideas and
   tell how it made the author
   feel.

3. How does the author help
   you picture the ideas in the
   story?

4. What lines, shapes, and
   colors would you use to
   make an exciting picture?

5. What do you see now as you
   look around?

Little Sounds

Beatrice Schenk de Regniers

Underneath the big sounds
underneath the big silences
listen for the little secret sounds.

Listen.
ts ts
That is the little sound of the sugar,
the little loaf of sugar
deep inside the cup of hot black coffee.
ts ts
That is what the sugar says.

Listen for the little secret sounds.

Sh! be very quiet and listen.

tck tck tck tck tck tck tck tck

That is the little sound of your father's
  watch.

tck tck tck tck tck tck tck tck

It makes such a tiny hurrying scurrying
  sound.

Listen for the little sounds always.

When a pussycat licks her fur

can you hear a little sound?

When someone is licking an ice-cream cone

can you hear?

Did you ever hear
a rabbit biting a lettuce leaf?
a cow switching her tail?
a tiny baby breathing?

Listen
to the little sound of
a letter dropping into a letter box,
a pin falling to the floor,
a leaf falling from a tree,
dry leaves crunching under your feet.

Listen to the little secret sound
of a pencil writing on paper,
of a scissors snipping your fingernails,
of a flower stem breaking when you pick
    a flower.

Listen for the little sounds always—
listen.

The World Is Full of Wonderful Smells
Zhenya Gay

The world is full of wonderful smells,
And you have a nose that always tells
Of bread in the oven, hot and nice,
Of cake being baked with lots of spice,
Of a barn with fresh-cut hay in the mows,
Of horses and pigs and cats and cows,
Of a dog when he's warm and lies in the sun,
Of applesauce and chocolate and a sugar bun.
Wouldn't it be dreadful if you'd no nose to tell
Of every wonderful, wonderful smell?

What's the Funniest Thing?

Beatrice Schenk de Regniers

What's the funniest thing you can think of?
What's the funniest thing you can think of?
   A monkey doing tricks?
   A house built out of sticks?
   An elephant juggling bricks?
What's the funniest thing *you* can think of?

What's the saddest thing you can think of?
What's the saddest thing you can think of?
   To see a puppy cry?
   Or a bird that cannot fly?
   Or to have to say good-by?
What's the saddest thing *you* can think of?

What's the noisiest thing you can think of?
What's the noisiest thing you can think of?
　　One hundred birds chirping?
　　A great giant burping?
　　Ten soup slurpers slurping?
What's the noisiest thing *you* can think of?

What's the quietest thing you can think of?
What's the quietest thing you can think of?
   Grass growing?
   Snow snowing?
   A soft breeze blowing?
What's the quietest thing *you* can think of?

Keep a Poem in Your Pocket

Beatrice Schenk de Regniers

Keep a poem in your pocket
and a picture in your head
and you'll never feel lonely
at night when you're in bed.

The little poem will sing to you
the little picture bring to you
a dozen dreams to dance to you
at night when you're in bed.

So—
Keep a picture in your pocket
and a poem in your head
and you'll never feel lonely
at night when you're in bed.

(Acknowledgments continued from page 4.)

"Us Two," from the book *Now We Are Six* by A. A. Milne. Decorated by E. H. Shepard. Copyright 1927 by E. P. Dutton & Co., Inc. Renewal © 1955 by A. A. Milne. Reprinted by permission of the publishers.

"Rumpelstiltzkin," reprinted by permission of David McKay Company, Inc. from *The Blue Fairy Book* by Andrew Lang. Copyright 1948 by David McKay Company, Inc.

"What Witches Do," from *Is Somewhere Always Far Away?* by Leland B. Jacobs. Copyright © 1967 by Leland B. Jacobs. Reprinted by permission of Holt, Rinehart and Winston, Inc.

"Lazy Jack," reprinted by permission of G. P. Putnam's Sons from *Chimney Corner Stories* by Veronica S. Hutchinson. Copyright 1925 by Minton, Balch & Co.

"The Best Game the Fairies Play," from *Fairies and Chimneys* by Rose Fyleman. Copyright 1918, 1920 by George H. Doran Company. Reprinted by permission of Doubleday & Company, Inc., and The Society of Authors as the literary representative of the Estate of Rose Fyleman.

"Sleeping Beauty" by Jakob and Wilhelm Grimm. Courtesy of *Childcraft—The How and Why Library*.

"Some One" by Walter de la Mare. By permission of The Literary Trustees of Walter de la Mare and The Society of Authors as their representative.

The Story of Ferdinand by Munro Leaf and Robert Lawson. Copyright 1936 by Munro Leaf and Robert Lawson. Illustrations by Robert Lawson. Copyright © renewed 1964 by Munro Leaf and John W. Boyd. Reprinted by permission of The Viking Press, Inc.

Dandelion by Don Freeman. Copyright © 1964 by Don Freeman. Illustrations by Don Freeman. All rights reserved. Reprinted by permission of The Viking Press, Inc.

"The Monkeys and the Crocodile," from *Tirra Lirra* by Laura E. Richards. Published by Little, Brown and Company.

The Poppy Seed Cakes by Margery Clark. Illustrations by Maud and Miska Petersham. Copyright 1924 by Doubleday & Company, Inc. Reprinted by permission of Doubleday & Company, Inc.

"The Reason for the Pelican." Copyright © 1955 by The Curtis Publishing Company. From the book *The Reason for the Pelican* by John Ciardi. Copyright © 1959 by John Ciardi. Reprinted by permission of J. B. Lippincott Company.

Frederick by Leo Lionni. Copyright © 1967 by Leo Lionni. Illustrations by Leo Lionni. Reprinted by permission of Pantheon Books, a division of Random House, Inc.

Do You See What I See? by Helen Borten. Illustrations by Helen Borten. Reprinted by permission of Abelard-Schuman, Ltd. All Rights Reserved. Copyright 1959.

"Little Sounds," from *Something Special*, text © 1958 by Beatrice Schenk de Regniers; illustrations © 1958 by Irene Haas. Reprinted by permission of Harcourt Brace Jovanovich, Inc.

"The World Is Full of Wonderful Smells," from *Jingle Jangle* by Zhenya Gay. Copyright 1953 by Zhenya Gay. Reprinted by permission of The Viking Press, Inc.

"What's the Funniest Thing?" and "Keep a Poem in Your Pocket," from *Something Special*, text © 1958 by Beatrice Schenk de Regniers; illustrations © 1958 by Irene Haas. Reprinted by permission of Harcourt Brace Jovanovich, Inc.

Illustrators

George Albertus—"The Chimpanzee That Mopped the Floor"
David Broad—"Afternoon with Grandmother," "Sleeping Beauty"
Ray Der—"The Ice-Cream Man," "Wind Song," "The World Is Full of Wonderful Smells"
Lowell Herrero—"That's My Favorite"
Michael Maggid—"The Park," "Where Go the Boats?"
Victor Moscosso—"Rumpelstiltzkin"
Carol Robson—"What Witches Do," "Some One"
Dugald Stermer—"Picnics"
Ed Taber—"Lazy Jack," "The Best Game the Fairies Play," "The Monkeys and the Crocodile"
Wendy Wheeler—"Bumble Bee," "The Reason for the Pelican"
Sue Gilmour: Unit Openers

224